Peace
is an
Offering

Peace is

Words by
Annette LeBox

SCHOLASTIC INC.

an
Offering

pictures by
Stephanie Graegin

For Charly, hugs —ALB

For my siblings —SG

ISBN 978-1-338-18847-9

12 11 10 9 8 7 6   19 20 21 22

Printed in the U.S.A.   40

First Scholastic printing, April 2017

Designed by Lily Malcom
Text set in Fiesole
The illustrations were rendered in pencil and watercolor and then assembled and colored digitally.

Peace is an offering.
A muffin or a peach.

A birthday invitation.

A trip to the beach.

Peace is gratitude for simple things.

Light through a leaf, a dragonfly's wings.

A kiss on the cheek, raindrops and dew.
A walk in the park, a bowl of hot stew.

Peace is holding on to another.

Peace is the words you say to a brother.

Will you stay with me?
Will you be my friend?
Will you listen to my story
till the very end?

Will you wait when I'm slow?
Will you calm my fears?
Will you sing to the sun
to dry my tears?

Will you keep me company when I'm all alone?
Will you give me shelter when I've lost my home?

You might find peace in a photograph,

Or in the deep boom of a belly laugh.

And even in the wake of tragedy,
Even then, you might find her.
In the rubble of a fallen tower.
In the sorrow of your darkest hour.
In the hat of a hero.
In the loss of a friend.

Peace is a joining, not a pulling apart.
It's the courage to bear a wounded heart.

It's a safe place to live.
It's the freedom from fear.

It's a kiss or a hug
When you've lost someone dear.

So offer a cookie,

Walk away from a fight.

Comfort a friend
Through the long, dark night.

Sing a quiet song.

Catch a falling star.

May peace walk beside you
Wherever you are.

Annette LeBox

is a conservationist and award-winning author. She divides her time between her home in Maple Ridge, British Columbia, Canada, and her remote cabin in the Cariboo grasslands.

Stephanie Graegin

spent her childhood drawing and collecting fauna. These days, she lives in Brooklyn, is still drawing, and has managed to keep her animal collection down to one orange cat.